Quirky Wa... Pop Songs

A great collection of 10 easy-to-play songs

WISE PUBLICATIONS
part of The Music Sales Group
London/New York/Paris/Sydney/Copenhagen/Berlin/Madrid/Tokyo

Published by
Wise Publications
14-15 Berners Street,
London W1T 3LJ, UK.

Exclusive Distributors:
Music Sales Limited
Distribution Centre, Newmarket Road,
Bury St Edmunds, Suffolk IP33 3YB, UK.

Music Sales Pty Limited
120 Rothschild Avenue,
Rosebery, NSW 2018,
Australia.

Order No. AM987976
ISBN 1-84609-803-3
This book © Copyright 2006 by Wise Publications,
a division of Music Sales Limited.

Arranging & Engraving supplied by Camden Music.
Music edited by Ann Farmer.
Compiled by Nick Crispin.

Printed in the EU.

Cover photograph courtesy of iStock International Inc.

Your Guarantee of Quality
As publishers, we strive to produce every book to the highest commercial standards.
The music has been carefully designed to minimise awkward page turns and to make playing from it a real pleasure.
Particular care has been given to specifying acid-free, neutral-sized paper made from pulps
which have not been elemental chlorine bleached. This pulp is from farmed sustainable forests
and was produced with special regard for the environment.
Throughout, the printing and binding have been planned to ensure
a sturdy, attractive publication which should give years of enjoyment.
If your copy fails to meet our high standards, please inform us and
we will gladly replace it.

www.musicsales.com

Bridget the Midget

Words & Music by Ray Stevens

1. Well, come on down_
(Verse 2 see additional lyrics)

_ to the go - go,_ down on the strip. If you wan-na get hip to a brand new trip, they got a

Ev-'ry - bo-dy sock it to me: Yo_____ oh

oh,_____

Audience response

Yo_____ oh,

Audience response

oh,_____   Oh,___ yeah._____

Audience response

C

___   Well, come on,   ev-'ry bo-dy, have you

6

2. Well, she may be small, just two feet tall,
   But if you give her half a chance and she'll pin you to a wall,
   She's a little showstopper, you're gonna have a ball,
   She can sing, she can dance, she can really do it all, yeah!

3. *(Spoken)* Thank you folks, thank you! Ha ha! I wanna know something...do ya feel alright?
   Aww, come on now...you can do better than that! Do ya feel alright?
   Wow! Haha! You know that makes me feel...so good!
   Let me hear it again...do ya feel alright?

Funky Gibbon

Words & Music by Bill Oddie

It's not hard, so let's all do the fun-ky gib-bon, ooh, ooh, ooh!

Do, do, do, the fun-ky gib-bon. (The fun-ky gib-bon.)

We are here to show you how.____ (Ooh, ooh, ooh!)

Ooh, ooh, ooh, the fun-ky gib-bon. (The fun-ky gib-bon.) He's

in a while you'll start to smile,_ gib-bon half a chance._ Do, do, do, the fun-ky

gib-bon. We are here to show you how._

(Ooh, ooh, ooh!) Ooh, ooh, ooh, the fun-ky

gib-bon. (The fun-ky gib-bon.) He's just like you so come on do the

Now, everybody get ready to do the funky gibbon!

fun - ky gib - bon now.____ Ooh, ooh, the fun - ky gib - bon.

Ooh, ooh, ooh, the fun - ky gib - bon. Ooh, ooh, ooh, the fun - ky gib - bon.

Ooh, ooh, ooh, the fun - ky gib - bon. Drop one arm down by your knees, let the

oth-er arm reach up to the trees.___ Let your wrist go limp like a bent bab - boon, and get

read-y to sing___ this gib-bon's tune.___ Now will you

give me an 'Ooh', Ooh, will you give me an-oth-er 'Ooh', Ooh, will you give me an 'Ooh', Ooh, now

D.S. al Coda

put 'em tog-eth-er___ and what have you got? Ooh, ooh, ooh, *etc.*

⊕ *Coda*

C

fun - ky gib - bon now.___ Ooh, ooh, ooh, the fun - ky gib - bon,

Verse 3:

Gee, the world would be good,

I know how nice it could be,

With just a little gibbon take (sha, la, la, la).

Be just like a gibbon,

Oh, feel the rhythm,

An' you'll agree, you'll dance up to,

The Planet of the Apes.

14

Lily The Pink

Traditional
Arranged by John Gorman, Roger McGough & Mike McGear

March-like ♩ = 110

N.C.

Chorus: We'll drink a drink a drink to Li-ly the pink the pink the pink, the sav-iour of ___ the hum-an race. ___ For she in-vent-ed ___ med-ic-in-al

com - pound,_____ most ef - fi - ca - cious_____ in ev - 'ry case.

1. Mis - ter Fre - ars_____ hadstick-y out ea - rs_____ and it
(Verses 3, 5 & 7 see block lyrics)

made him aw - ful shy._____ And so they gave him

med-ic- in - al com - pound_____ and now he's learn - ing_____ how to

6. Jen -ni - fer Ecc - les_____ had ter -ri - ble freck - les_____ and the

boys all call her names._____ But she changed with med -ic - in - al

com - pound,_____ now he joins_____ in all their games.

We'll_____

D.S. al Coda 3

19

Coda 3

Rubato

8. Up to heav - en her soul_ as - cend - ed oh the

church bells they did ring._____ She took with her med - ic - in - al

com - pound; hark! The her - ald ang - els sing. *Chorus:* We'll

a tempo

drink a drink a drink to Li - ly the pink the pink the pink, the sav - iour

Verse 3:
Old Ebenezer thought he was Julius Caesar,
And so they put him in a home,
Where they gave him medicinal compound,
And now he's Emperor of Rome.

Verse 5:
Aunty Millie ran willy-nilly,
When her legs they did recede,
And so they rubbed on medicinal compound,
Now they call her Millepede.

Verse 7:
Lily the pink she, turned to drink she,
Filled up with paraffin inside,
And despite her medicinal compound,
Sadly Picca-Lily died.

Goodbye-ee

Words & Music by Dudley Moore & Peter Cooke

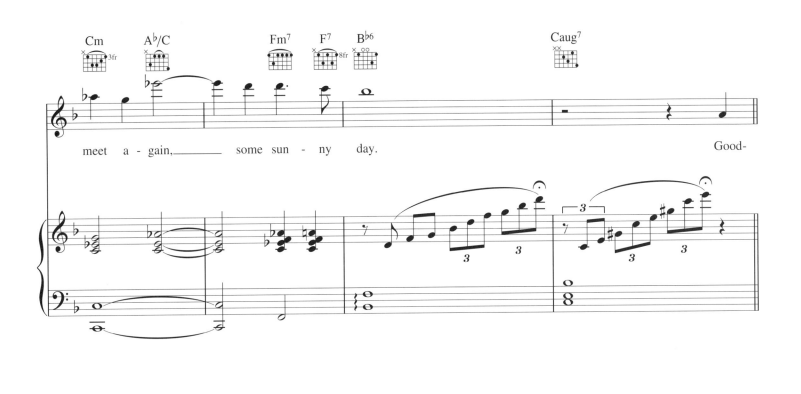

meet a-gain,_____ some sun-ny day.

Good-

Foxtrot, with a light touch ♩ = 96

- bye, good-bye, we're leav-ing you skid-dle-ey da, good -

(See spoken block lyrics on repeat)

- bye,_____ we bid you fond good-bye. Fa-ta ta-ta,___ fa-ta ta-ta.___ Good-

bye, good - bye, we're leav - ing you skidd-le - ey da, good -

- bye,_____ we bid you fond good - bye. La - da__ da da da. La - da

da, da, la - da da - da._____

La - da__ da, da, da. Uh, da, da, da, da, da, da. Good-bye,__

Spoken over repeated section:

You know there comes a time in everybody's life when they must say goodbye. That time is now.
And so, with tears in either eye, we say goodbye as people have said throughout the years.
We leave this mortal coil on which we strut and fret our weary way as Shakespeare put it. God bless him.
What a wonderful, old chap Shakespeare was. Bald, but sexy. Oh, take that rhythm away with its wonderful
melodies. Oh, goodbye they say. Goodbye, why not say it again? Goodbye *etc.*

Itsy Bitsy Teenie Weenie Yellow Polka Dot Bikini

Words & Music by Paul Vance & Lee Pockriss

Verse 2:

She was afraid to come out in the open,

And so a blanket around her she wore.

She was afraid to come out in the open,

And so she sat bundled up on the shore, two, three, four,

Tell the people what she wore.

Mmm Mmm Mmm Mmm

Words & Music by Brad Roberts

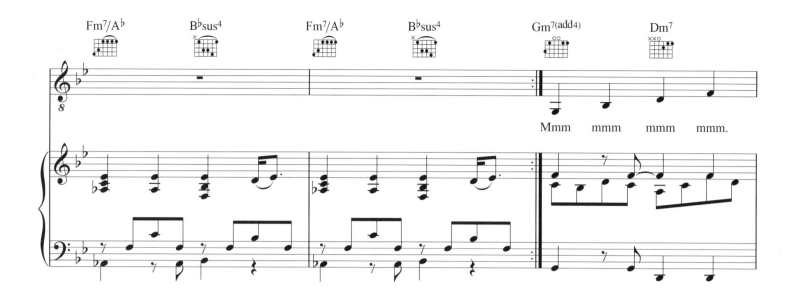

Mmm mmm mmm mmm.

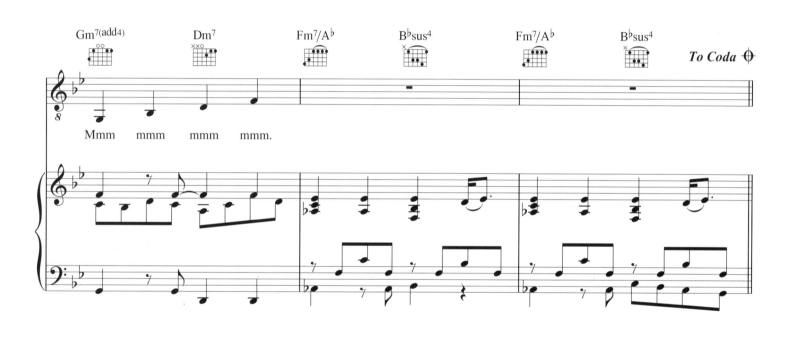

Mmm mmm mmm mmm.

To Coda ⊕

3. And though the girl and boy were___ glad, but one kid had it

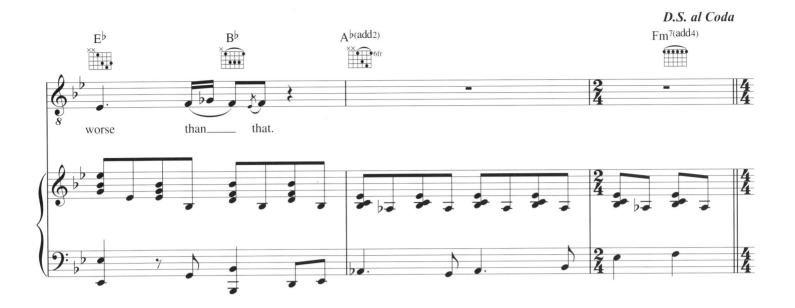

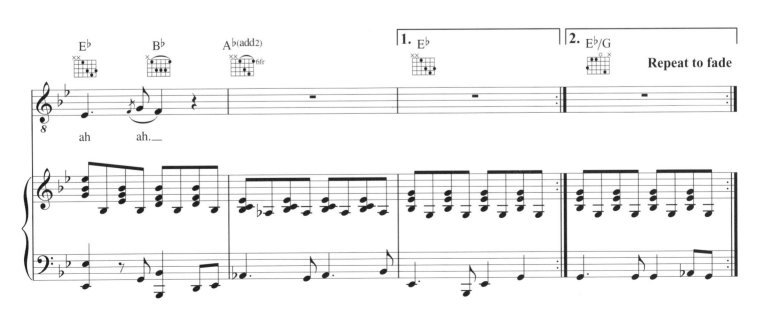

33

Shaddap You Face

Words & Music by Joe Dolce

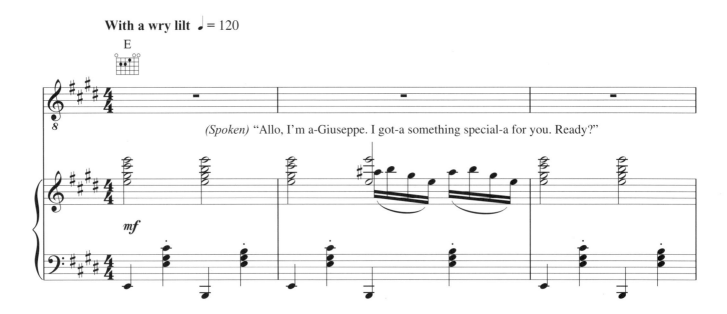

What's-a mat-ter you? Hey! Got-ta no res-pect. What do you think you do?

Why you look-a so sad? It's-a not so bad, it's a nice-a place. Ah shad-

-up-pa you face! *(Spoken)* That's-a my Mamma. Can-a remember it. Big accordion solo!

36

Soon there'll come a day gon - na be a big - a star.___ Then -

- a make T. V. shows and - a mo - vies,___ get - a my - self a new car. But still I be my - self, I don't

D.S. al Coda

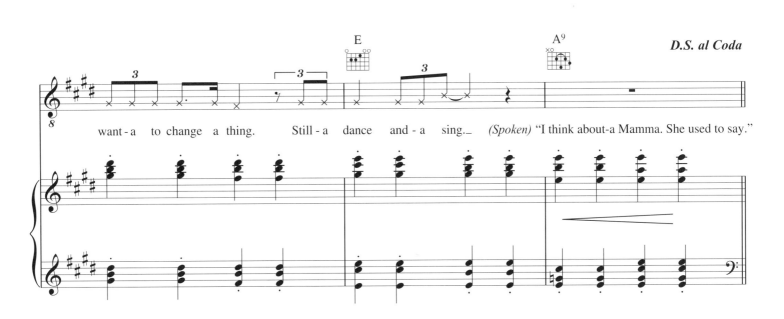

want - a to change a thing. Still - a dance and - a sing.___ *(Spoken)* "I think about - a Mamma. She used to say."

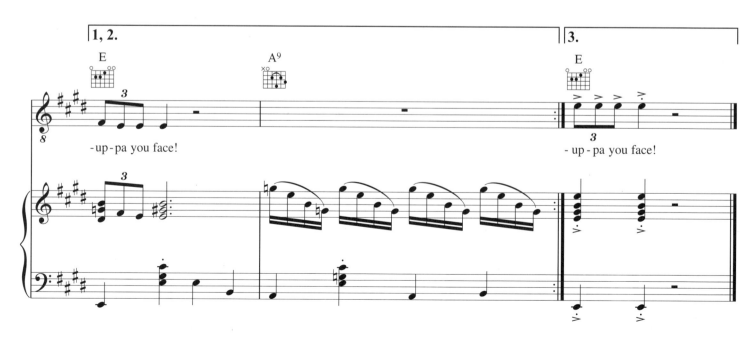

Walk The Dinosaur

Words & Music by David Was, Don Was & Randall Jacobs

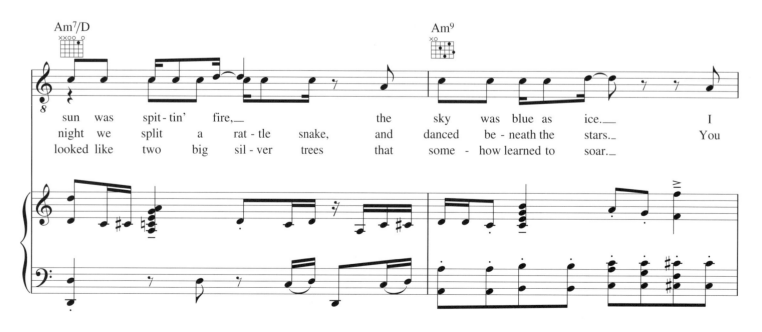

42

One night_ I dreamed of_ New York. You and_ I roast - ing_ blue

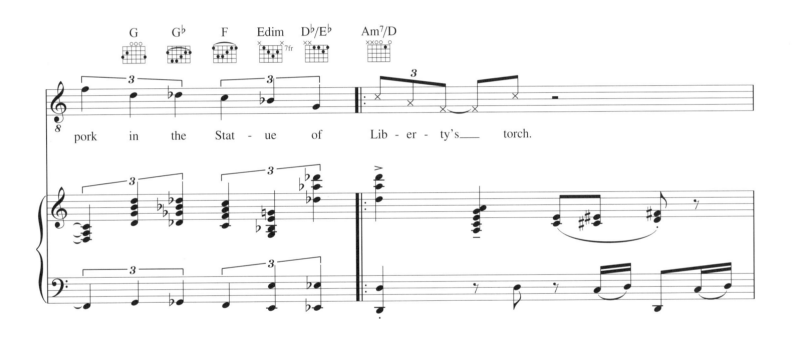

pork in the Stat - ue of Lib - er - ty's_ torch.

D.S. al Fine

43

Yakety Yak

Words & Music by Jerry Leiber & Mike Stoller

45

Wooly Bully

Words & Music by Domingo Samudio

U - no,__ dos, one, two, tres, qua - tro...

(Sax solo on ℅)

1. Mat - ty told   Hat - ty   a - bout a   thing   she   saw,_____
2. Mat - ty told   Hat - ty   "Let's don't take   no   chance.____
3. Mat - ty told   Hat - ty   "It's the   thing   to   do._____

had   two___ big   horns_____   and a
Let's   not   be   L - se - ven,   come and
Get   you some-one real - ly   to   pull the

wool - y   jaw._____   Wool - y
learn   to   dance."____ } Wool - y   Bull - y._____   Wool - y
wool   with   you."____